A Picture History of Margaret Catchpole

by Richard Cobbold

edited by Pip Wright

Other books by Pip Wright
Lydia
Death Recorded
I Read it in the local Rag (pub. by Poppyland Publishing)
Exploring Suffolk by Bus Pass
Thomas Slapp's Booke of Physicke

Books by Pip & Joy Wright
The Amazing Story of John Heigham Steggall,
'The Suffolk Gipsy' (ed. by Richard Cobbold)
Newspapers in Suffolk (6 vols)
Grave Reports
Witches in and around Suffolk
Bygone Cotton

See all these at **www.pipwright.com**

&
The Diary of a Poor Suffolk Woodman
(with Léonie Robinson, pub. by Poppyland Publishing) see **www.poppyland.co.uk**

A Picture History of Margaret Catchpole

a reduced-text version of the book by
Richard Cobbold with 33 original
illustrations by the author

edited by Pip Wright

Rev. Richard Cobbold

ISBN 978-0-9548298-8-9

Published by **Pawprint Publishing**
14, Polstead Close, Stowmarket, Suffolk   IP14 2PJ

Acknowledgements
Special thanks are owed to Anthony Cobbold of the Cobbold Family History Trust
(see page 129) and the many generous subscribers to the appeal fund which saved
Richard Cobbold's charming illustrations and ensured they would remain in England.
Thanks to Des Herring for reference to his data file on Suffolk pubs.
We are specially grateful to Colchester and Ipswich Museums for use of the picture on page 122
Also, I had help from a number of people who live in places
close to those associated with this story. As always with my books,
I have relied on help and advice from those at the Suffolk Record Offices.

Introduction

In February 1845, the Ipswich Journal and Suffolk Chronicle carried an advert for a new publication, *'The History of Margaret Catchpole, a Suffolk Girl.'* In three volumes and priced initially at one guinea, the book promised to tell the remarkable story of a girl whose name was still familiar to many in the Ipswich area, even though she had been transported to Australia nearly half a century earlier.

The author was the Rev. Richard Cobbold, Rector of Wortham. A set of watercolours had been painted by him to serve as illustrations for the book, but few of these pictures were ever used and they were rarely reproduced in colour. Towards the end of his life, Cobbold had them bound into an album along with observations he thought to scribble alongside at a later date. This collection of illustrations and Cobbold's notes remained hidden until they appeared recently for auction. They are now in the care of the Cobbold Family History Trust, who are as keen as I am to share them with the people of Suffolk and beyond.

The story was a best-seller and has continued to be published, on and off, until the present day. Plays have been written about Margaret Catchpole. There is even a pub named after her; and she is still more celebrated in Australia, where she spent the last third of her life.

Richard Cobbold was intrigued by the story, as his family were involved in a major way. Though Cobbold was little more than a babe in arms when Margaret was transported, he grew up hearing about her and knew many of the characters whose names grace the tale.

Much has been made in the past of the way Richard Cobbold romanticised the story of Margaret Catchpole. He certainly made her younger, prettier, and somehow contrived to make her a paragon of virtue in spite of her crimes and criminal misjudgements. Details of the story can, in the cold light of day, be shown to offer an alternative version of history. Still, it was a novel, as he claimed, substantially true, but embellished to make it more entertaining. It was written half a century after the event by someone who hadn't witnessed any of it. Research then was less precise than it is now and it seems likely that Cobbold was intending to tweak history rather than radically rewrite it.

So what we have here is a rattling good tale; for the first time told through the pictures Richard Cobbold painted for it. The text has been much reduced from the original. Three printing styles are used…

One represents extracts from the original novel.

Another is to show Cobbold's notes, written in later life when he was 77 years old. Occasionally where words could not be understood, I have attempted to guess his intentions from the context, and believe this to be a fair interpretation of his writing.

The third style is used for my own précis of events, to help speed the story along

Pip Wright

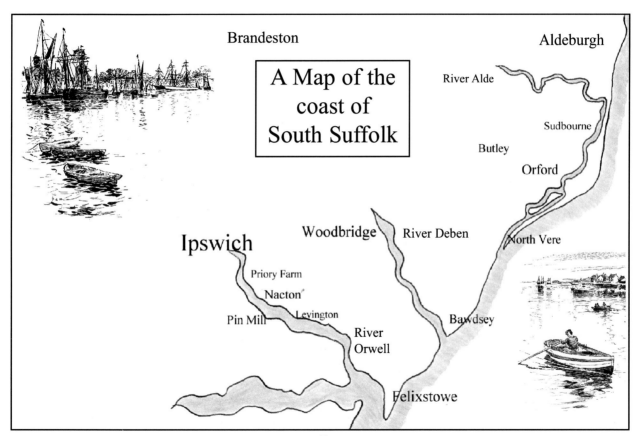

A Map of the coast of South Suffolk

Brandeston

Aldeburgh

River Alde

Sudbourne

Butley

Orford

Ipswich

Woodbridge

River Deben

North Vere

Priory Farm

Nacton

Pin Mill

Levington

River Orwell

Bawdsey

Felixstowe

*WRITTEN AT THE AGE OF 77 - We begin our illustrations of Margaret Catchpole with a view of the town of Ipswich, as it was in days gone by before all the various improvements of a wet dock, and hanging gardens hid the semicircular laps of the River Orwell from the banks of the Common Quay. This sketch was made from the corner of the Cliff garden wall where stood some fine old trees on the Cliffs that then overhung the river. I myself often sketched those trees. There I stood with dear and dearest friends, when the Orwell East Indiaman was launched from Bayley's Shipyard on the opposite side of the River - a memorable day because I then made the offer of my hand and heart to a young lady, who has now been my dear Wife 52 years (1874). But all things change! What revolutions of empires have we seen since then - All Australia has become peopled with civilized and colonised people since then. And two John Cobbolds have become MP for Ipswich since then. The Poor Old Parish Parson or Pastor, The Author of Margaret Catchpole and his wife are still alive and hope to live for ever - not here but elsewhere. He cannot forget however that all his children were born in the same room on St. Margaret's Green.

*It is worth noting that you, the reader, may find these asides from Richard Cobbold a little distracting. They are not essential to an enjoyment of the story, but are included for their historical value. At times, he rambles a little, and at times his comments are hard to follow. However, they are a valuable insight as to how this story came to be written.

Margaret Catchpole was born at Nacton at that place they called the Seven Hills. Her father Jonathan Catchpole was a labourer, and his youngest daughter became used to riding and working with horses from an early age. They and their nearest neighbours, the Cracknells, worked on the lands of Mr. Denton.

As the youngest but one of a family of six, Margaret became responsible for much of the care of her older sister Susan, who was **of a sickly constitution and very delicate: she had little bodily strength, but she had learned to knit and sew, and in these things she excelled.**

The Catchpoles' cottage at Seven Hills, Nacton was some distance from the River Orwell. It was demolished many years later, and a number of chestnut trees planted in its place.

When Margaret was just thirteen, **her mother one day sent her down to the farmhouse to ask for a little broth, which had been promised by Mrs Denton, her mistress, for poor Susan. When Margaret arrived at the gate, she heard a shriek from a female in the house and in another minute she was in the kitchen, where the mistress of the house had suddenly fallen down in a fit.**

Margaret wasted no time. She calmed the servant and made her mistress comfortable before running to where the Suffolk punches were stabled. Without saddle or bridle, she mounted one and rode full-pelt towards Ipswich and the house of Doctor Stebbing.

She passed every cart jogging on to Ipswich market without taking any notice of the drivers, though she knew many of them well. She even met Admiral Vernon's carriage just as she turned on to the Ipswich racecourse at the part now called Nacton Corner. At length she reached the end of the racecourse and came on to the common of Bishop's Hill. Down she dashed into the very thickest part of the back hamlet of St. Clements. People gave way as she rode fearlessly on over the stone pavement to Orwell Place, where lived the ever humane though eccentric surgeon, Mr. George Stebbing. The very moment the door was opened and the doctor himself appeared, she exclaimed. "Oh come to my mistress, sir, directly! - come to my mistress."

The good doctor returned to Nacton with Margaret in his gig beside him, to discover Mrs. Denton was much better, largely as a result of Margaret's calmness in treating her. As a result of this, Margaret was highly thought of by all who knew her, and the memory of her intrepid ride would ensure her a good job in the future. When Doctor Stebbing took leave of the family, he told Margaret **that if ever she stood in need of a friend to help her, she only had to "post off again for the doctor."**

MARGARET RIDING FOR THE DOCTOR - This is a vivid sketch of young W Harpur trying to catch Margaret who was riding for Dr. Stebbing; and such a fete was the cause of her introduction to the Cliff (as I have heard) Be it as you may you will see the spirit of the Author in this little Race course sketch. I was upset with Mr. Glyde's finding fault with me for the want of obtaining accurate information of that day. He says of poor me that I was educated at Ipswich Grammar School - now the school is in existence and had he taken the pains to enquire locally he would have found that I never had the honour to be a boy at Ipswich Grammar School (Never). I went to Bury at six years old - now what reason has such a man to boast of my inaccuracy, when his own and the means close at hand might have been consulted by him. Accept then the sketch and let critics bark though they cannot bite.

Early into our story comes a young man by the name of William Laud. His father ran a ferry-boat between Harwich and Landguard Point. Will Laud began his working days apprenticed to a boat-builder and studied navigation. His father hoped his son would find honest service. Unfortunately, he came to know a certain Captain Bargood, who persuaded the young man to lead a team of smugglers running contraband from the Low Countries to the Suffolk coast.

William Laud and Margaret met at a christening and were very much taken with one another. But sickly sister Susan did not trust this man, and with her last breath made this prediction…

"Margaret, you will never marry William Laud - he will cause you all much sorrow; but do not forsake the right and honest path and you will find peace at the last."

William Laud, give him his due, did look for ways to live an honest life, but again and again Captain Barwood and his shipmate, John Luff, coaxed him back to life as a smuggler, from whence he was able to send Margaret rich presents. She guessed what work had paid for these and when a seaman came to her door with another bundle of silks and lace, ribbons and tea; enough to stock a shop, she shouted, **"You may take the whole bundle back and tell the young man who gave it to you I should have valued one single pair of honestly purchased gloves more than all the valuables he has sent me."**

In the course of time, Will Laud's gang became notorious. **At Bawdsey Cliff, the smugglers had a cave of no small dimensions** where booty was stored. It was rumoured, they had many other such stores along the coast of Suffolk.

Around this time, Margaret's elder brother Charles left the family home. Under the name of Jacob Dedham, he signed and enlisted in an army regiment bound for the East Indies. It would be many years before any of the family would see him again.

Margaret heard from time to time from Will Laud, but rarely saw him in person. She gave away most of the presents he sent. For all that, people shunned the Catchpole family on account of their attachment to the smuggler, and they fell on hard times.

Then, **a dreadful conflict took place below Felixstowe beach between the coastguard and Laud's crew.** Headed by Lieutenant Edward Barry, the preventative service officer, they surprised the smugglers. **Three of the crew were killed and the others, unable to stand against the assault, fled as well as they were able. Young Barry and Laud had a severe personal encounter in which the death of one or the other seemed the determination of both.**

Barry was the better swordsman. However, the night was dark and Laud drew the first blood; but a cut of the blade across his forehead left Will Laud severely wounded. John Luff, Will Laud's smuggler colleague appeared on the scene. Himself wounded and believing Laud to be good as dead, Edward Barry retreated, leaving Luff on the beach to attend to his wounded captain.

But Luff had thrown him over his shoulder and, being well acquainted with the marshes, had carried him over some planks and had escaped.

An eighteenth century coastguardman

17

The people of that part of Suffolk believed William Laud was dead. So did Margaret, until a sailor came one day to convey her to a cottage on Walton Cliff where she found him sick and in much pain. Helping to nurse him back to health, she tried her best to convince him to choose a new life now. But visits from Captain Barwood and John Luff increased as he grew better, and Margaret knew by the time she left him, it was a vain hope that he would change his criminal ways. Yet the longer she put trust in his changing and **the more she excused his past life, the more deeply her heart became engaged to him.**

Margaret, true to her intentions of going to service, found a kind friend in Mrs. Denton, who recommended her to Mrs. Wake of the Priory Farm, Downham Reach. Here, in September, 1792, she took up her abode as servant-of-all-work.

Gainsborough Lane,
leading down to Priory Farm

Margaret was highly regarded by her employers and all the others who worked at the farm, none moreso than John Barry, brother of Edward Barry, the coastguardman who had so nearly been the cause of the death of her lover, Will Laud. John Barry was an honest and industrious young man, son of the miller at Levington, and as his love and admiration for Margaret grew, he was unable to keep it to himself any longer.

Piper's Vale, Ipswich,
close to Alnesbourn Priory

THE PRIORY FARM - This (now farm house called Pond Hall) was the place where Margaret first went to service. My informant thereof was Dr. Stebbing who I think was the first to commend Margaret Catchpole for a servant to my Mother, Mrs. Elizabeth Cobbold. It is still a very picturesque spot and has been very nicely sketched by Mrs. _____. Many are the pencil drawings I have made of this and other lovely spots in Gainsborough Lane leading to Downham Reach. That is not Will Laud crossing the footbridge but John Barry a labourer on the farm - There is hardly a prettier little nook on the Banks of the Orwell than this spot in the Valley of Alneshborne.

Priory Farm, now known as Pond Hall

One evening, returning home from work, Barry told Margaret of his love for her. It came as no real surprise. She had noticed the way he looked at her. Of course, he believed that Will Laud was dead. In order not to raise his hopes, she had to tell John Barry that the smuggler was very much alive. But she swore him to secrecy to keep that information to himself.

Meanwhile, Will Laud had been living just up the coast in a small cottage close to Butley Abbey. He had been captaining his ship, the Stour, under the name of Hudson, whilst pretending to Margaret that his smuggling days were over.

"I think I shall leave the service and marry," he announced to his shipmate, John Luff.

"And get a halter for your pains! No, Will; no, my boy; you are made of sterner stuff than that."

John Luff's opinion was that he should marry the girl, across the sea in Holland if necessary, but retirement, even now would leave him ever in fear of being arrested for his past crimes.

"But Margaret supposes me at this moment in a foreign ship, and in an honest trader."

"Let her think so still. Only once get her on board the Stour, and never trust me if we don't quickly run over to Holland, get you decently married and you may settle with her on shore in a short time."

That was the plan - how it worked was like this - At the very end of September, just before the Harvest celebrations, a sailor turned up at Priory Farm. He spoke like a Dutchman and claimed to be one of Will Laud's crew. He said that Laud wanted to meet with Margaret.

It was all arranged that she should be on the shore at nine o'clock, and look out for a small sail-boat, which should come up the river and run ashore against the creek: that the watchword should be "*Margaret*," and that punctuality should be observed.

She had no idea she was to be kidnapped.

John Barry did not enjoy the Harvest celebrations that year. The girl he loved had turned him down. So he left the farmhouse where others were drinking and making merry, and found himself walking the foreshore close to the gamekeeper's cottage below Orwell Park, heading towards his family home at Levington.

Another character was on the river that night, **the ancient fisherman, Thomas Colson, but better known by the appellation of Robinson Crusoe. His little vessel presented a curious specimen of naval patchwork, for his extreme poverty did not afford him the means of procuring proper materials. In this leaky and crazy vessel, it was his constant custom, by day and by night, in calms and in storms, to toil on the river for fish. With a mind somewhat distempered and faculties impaired, he was a firm believer in the evil agency of witches and witchcraft.**

THOMAS COLSON - There is no character described in the History of Margaret Catchpole more singularly interesting or exciting than of this said Thomas Colson, and none more true. Very few are alive now (1874) who can remember the old Fisherman of the Orwell. In his day almost the only real fisherman on the River - Many a time have I run down the slope at the Cliff so to meet the old man, with his basket of fish to shew to my mother - All alive-o, soals, plaice, sandabs and eels - And then to hear him talk to Mrs Cobbold about his fiends, the different Demons who sometimes befriended him and sometimes opposed him. He was well read in a book of deep horoscopic literature called Saducission Triumphans - Did you, reader, ever see the Book (I have it). The history of this man will be found in the Suffolk Garland. Poor Fellow - a hard working industrious man. I wish he had been a Christian and the devils would have flown from him.

As Will Laud and John Luff sailed upriver under a clear moonlit sky, they encountered Thomas Colson as he fished the river.

"What ship ahoy?" called Colson

"It's only old Robinson Crusoe," said Laud to John Luff, expecting to hear nothing more.

"I know that's Will Laud's voice," came back the reply, **"though I haven't heard it lately."**

"Confound the fellow," muttered Will. **"I never heard him say so much before."** As they both passed Pin Mill, Colson sneered. In his eyes, the Devil had jumped from his own craft to the one passing.

"You've lightened my cargo," he called. **"You've got a pleasant companion aboard. You've got my black fiend on your mainsail."**

PIN MILL - This is the only sketch to which I as Author of the rest of the illustrations cannot lay claim except that it was given to me by the Lady who drew it - viz The Honourable Miss Townsend: sister of Lord Bayning - She gave it to me as one of her sketches from nature after permission to read the Ms of MC before publication. It is not the less valuable on that account: It is a fact that the Revd Mr Cross and the Hon Miss Bayning did sit up the whole night to read the Ms of Margaret Catchpole - so interesting was it to these noble minded ladies - I quite admire the sketch done from nature when these ladies were staying at Wolverstone.

Laud's little boat **came bounding to the shore. The watchword *'Margaret'* was spoken, and in another moment her love and hope were embodied in the embrace of him she loved.**

"Now, Margaret," he at length exclaimed. "Now's the time: my boat is ready, my ship is at the mouth of the river. A snug little cabin is at your service. I am come to take you to a country where we may be married, but if you send me away now, we may never meet again."

Nacton foreshore, looking towards Downham Reach

In all the time since Will Laud had nearly been killed, Margaret had heard nothing of his latest smuggling activities and had dared to believe he was now an honest man. She needed to be sure this was true and so she asked him to tell her the truth. He was not prepared to lie to her.

"My name has changed but not my nature. I am a smuggler still."

"No, William, no - you cannot be! You are in the service of an honest man, though he be a foreigner."

"No, Margaret I am not. You see before you the notorious Hudson. I am a smuggler still!"

Margaret had heard tales of Captain Hudson and his exploits and was horrified. **A giddiness overcame her,** and as the two smugglers tried to force her aboard, she felt powerless to resist.

John Luff grabbed hold of her. Margaret in terror shrieked aloud. Her cries echoed eerily along Downham Reach and were heard by another as he walked the riverside that night. John Barry became aware of her plight and he ran towards the source of the screams. He leapt down the low cliff and, seizing a strong breakwater stake, attacked the two smugglers. **"Villains release the girl!" was his exclamation.**

Against two armed ruffians, his plight should have been hopeless, but his first blow laid Luff low before a pistol shot from Laud struck him in the arm.

But assistance - unexpected assistance was at hand. A tall gaunt figure strode along the strand, armed with a long fisherman's pike or hook. It was old Colson, or poor Robinson Crusoe who was making his way with fish up the Orwell. He and young Barry, now side by side, beat back the smugglers to their boat. Then there was a flash and a loud explosion that left the generous, brave and faithful Barry stretched upon the sand.

JOHN BARRY ATTACKING WILL LAUD - This is the scene at the Priory Farm against the Gamekeepers Cottage wherein Jack Barry and old Colson bore such a conspicuous part in the preservation of Margaret - Poor old Colson, a real character! - But alas poor Author that is me when in the place of a real character when Margaret was dramatised they put in Gooseberry Pip seller of fruit. oh dear oh dear! But we must be subject to such absurdities. There is the old Gamekeeper Gooding's Cottage and there is the struggle between lawless authority and honest courage in a good cause. You must accept the sketch from the Author.

Meantime, Margaret had escaped. She rushed back to the Priory farm to raise the alarm. Young men ran as fast as they could down to the shore. Then, as Will Laud and John Luff escaped upriver, careful hands lifted the wounded Barry **as gently as they could; though the poor fellow groaned with the agony of his shattered arm and wounded side.**

Colson followed them, muttering curses - **"The foul fiend be with you! He'll consume you yet, ye cowards!"**

Those were dismal days for Margaret. **Certainly she owed her present safety to the intrepid boldness of the wounded man,** but she could not feel love for him to match her gratitude. Worse still, people now knew Will Laud was alive and a price was on his head.

Slowly, John Barry recovered and his love for Margaret never wavered. Yet she could not return that love, and in truth his survival had been most important to her so she then could be sure her lover would not be branded a murderer.

About the latter end of the ensuing November, Margaret returned to her parents. She had heard little of Will Laud. A watch was out for the smugglers and Margaret's lover had taken to the sea again, once more changing his name. At length, a report came of a sailor's death at Bawdsey Ferry and, fearing it was William, Margaret set out to view the body of the drowned man. But it was not Laud, and eventually such stories stopped altogether.

About this time, a new settlement was projected at New South Wales. One hundred acres of land for as many dollars were granted. Young Barry, his health much improved, begged his father to lend him the money to begin his life anew.

"Before I go," he said to Margaret, **"I must tell you as long as life holds in this heart of mine, I shall never love anyone else. I may prosper - I may be rich - I may be blessed with abundance - but I shall never be blessed with a wife."**

And as he left for a new world, he warned her one last time of the failings of the man she continued to love.

"He is not worthy of you. He will betray you. He will desert you. He will bring you to want, misery and ruin." Then he gave her a present - a small clasped Bible that had once belonged to his mother. Margaret had never learned to read, and it would be some time before she would realise just what a fine present that was.

Back home with her parents, life was hard. Early the following year, she lost her mother. There was a simple pauper's funeral. The family were not aware of a stranger arriving soon after who paid for the grave to be properly tended.

This same man made his way to the Catchpoles' cottage and claimed to have news of Margaret's brother, Charles, who had joined the army as a young man. Though at first they failed to recognise him, eventually the visitor revealed the fact that he was none other than Charles Catchpole, son and brother to Jonathan Catchpole and Margaret.

He regaled them with tales of his time in India and how he had become **an adept in all the cunning and customs of the various castes of natives in India,** to such an extent that he had become a spy for Lord Cornwallis **upon the frontier of Persia.**

THE SPY - The late Ed Bacon Esq. who had been many years in India gave me this sketch that is the original from which this is taken, together with Tabgur and he told me the narrative given in the life of Margaret - He employed this man to make him a sketch of Ipswich from Savage's Mill on Stoke Hills. How do feature and all things change around us. It is well that some narrate the incidents of their own Day. Or else all things would be forgotten. So you see I record things that happened in my day - the next is an accurate drawing by the same man.

Charles Catchpole carried with him a sketch of himself at Tabgur on the borders of Persia. He could only spend a few days with his family before sailing back to India.

TABGUR - This sketch (the original I mean) a larger one was given to me by Mr. Bacon, who bore witness to the accuracy and beauty of this self taught genius: He, to try his powers of delineation employed him to make a view of the Town of Ipswich - which is a very large and accurate drawing proving satisfactorily that the same hand did Tabgur on the frontier of Persia, did this also. The possessor of this book shall have that picture of Ipswich, if the same or desire for the same be intimated to the Author.

Never did Margaret see that brother again. She was shortly to change her place of abode. Her Uncle Leader who lived at Brandeston and who had a young family and was left a widower sought the assistance of his niece.

Her father, though he could but ill spare her, could see his daughter needed a change of scene and urged her to go.

No sooner had Margaret left for Brandeston than her father and younger brother Edward received visitors. Firstly the armed figures of Will Laud and John Luff appeared, rapidly followed by the coastguard. Though they had never helped or encouraged the smugglers, the Catchpoles were questioned at length. For these two honest men, to find themselves under suspicion was worrying.

"Father," said Edward when he was again seated by the fire, "I don't - I cannot like that fellow Laud, and how Margaret can endure him is to me strange."

His father shrugged his shoulders.

"She knew him, my boy, before he became the character he is now."

'Sot's Hole,' Brandeston, where Margaret went to live with her Uncle Leader.

Margaret was a good housekeeper and loved caring for her young cousins. Things might have remained that way, but her Uncle Leader **chose to take unto himself a new wife, a fat buxom widow of forty.**

Matters that had been Margaret's concern were taken out of her hands and she began to find herself in an increasingly uncomfortable situation. Her uncle's new wife found fault in all she did. She felt unwelcome where once she had been so happy. Then, one day, Will Laud appeared in the village. Margaret's uncle's new wife saw them together and **Mr. Leader, with a thousand exaggerations was informed of her outrageous conduct.** There was a loud and unforgiving row and things were said that they would all later regret.

> *THE PARTING - This represents Margaret in the act of parting with Will Laud and meeting Aunt Leader at the turn of the lane. I am in possession of a letter from the Revd Wm Tilney Spurdon Headmaster of North Walsham School who corroborates the narrative and says Aunt Leader came in, in a furious rage with her niece Margaret - He remembers the incident he says by the fact of his Uncle giving him sixpence for reading the History in the paper that day of the loss of the Royal George at Spithead. So if you find the date of that period it will tell you the date*. Moreover he states that he and Margaret went out and spent the 6d in sweetmeats and both made themselves ill.*

It had been only the shortest of visits from her lover, and a painful one at that. Will Laud was fevered and looking for ways of explaining away his past. He tried to convince Margaret that his next expedition for the smugglers would be his last, but she found this hard to believe, knowing the hold they seemed to have over him. **The farewell was spoken, and Laud departed. Margaret stood a moment with affectionate heart and tearful eye to watch his receding form.**

*The Royal George sank at Spithead with the loss of 900 lives on August 29th 1782, indicating a time scale in the life of Margaret that is somewhat removed from that suggested by Richard Cobbold. If she was born when Cobbold suggested, she would be just 9 years old then. In actual fact, she was about 20.

What was Margaret to do? Sent on her way by her uncle; abused by his new wife; and believing that her accidental meeting with Will Laud might prove her last.

Clutching her few possessions, Margaret found that the Bible that had been given her by John Barry attracted her attention. **It was a small clasped book, and, from being unable to read it, she had never made any outward parade of her possession of it. On now seeing it, she mechanically unclasped the book, and in the first page there lay a £5 banknote, and in the last page, another of the same value. What a treasure was here!**

This money, more than she had ever owned, gave her the confidence to make a decision about her future. She would not return home to Nacton. Remembering the promise the good Doctor Stebbing had once made about helping to find her a position in service, she found a carrier on his way to Ipswich and made for the Doctor's house in Orwell Place.

Six years had elapsed since Margaret's dramatic ride on behalf of Mrs. Denton and at first, the good doctor did not recognise her. But when Margaret told her who she was and how she was looking for work, he was as good as his word.

"Well, and what place do you want, my girl?"

"I can do any kind of plain work, sir, from the cow-house to the nursery."

"Nursery! Nursery! Do you know anything about the care of children?"

"I am very partial to children, sir, and children are very fond of me; my uncle had seven little ones and only me to look after them until he married again."

"Humph! - Well, go into the kitchen, my girl" - and here the kind-hearted man introduced her to his cook.

"Sally, this is the girl that rode the pony for the doctor; see and take care of her."

He had at that very time made up his mind to write a note of recommendation to a lady who lived at the Cliff, upon the banks of the Orwell. The lady he referred to was none other than Mrs. Elizabeth Cobbold, second wife of the Ipswich brewer John Cobbold Esq.

Shortly after this, and towards the end of May, Margaret was called to be introduced to her new Mistress. She found her in the company of two artists and old Thomas Colson, otherwise known as Robinson Crusoe. He had called at The Cliff to sell fish, but soon recognised the girl he had helped save from the smugglers at Downham Reach, some time before.

"Ah, is that you Peggy? It's many a long day since I've seen you. Have the fiends played you any more tricks?"

Mrs. Cobbold thought he was referring to the devils he was always complaining about.

"The foul fiend has long dwelt with her and hers, and you'll soon find that out. I've known her almost as long as I've known you, Ma'am; and if she's a-coming to your service, why, all I can say is, there will be pretty pranks a-going on in your house."

The lady evidently saw there was a mystery here, but knew better than to try and unravel the words and thoughts of the poor crazy old fisherman.

Margaret found the position a demanding one, **for she was under-nursemaid in the morning, and under-cook in the evening; two very different stations, but both of which she discharged with fidelity, and at length rose in that family to fill the head place in both stations at different periods.**

Mrs. Cobbold believed that all her servants should receive an education, and discovering Margaret to be illiterate, took it upon herself to instruct her new servant in reading and writing, **and rapid was the progress she made in everything explained to her.**

Margaret was an avid scholar, often attending lessons with the children in her charge, **and soon became as well-informed as any of the children. It was soon after this, she rose to be head nursemaid.**

As the winter came on, she would often walk beside the river, hoping to hear tidings of her lover, but no news was to be heard, good or bad.

During the coldest months, large flocks of wildfowl would gather on the Orwell, prompting sportsmen of all ages to come for the shooting.

Master William, one of the younger Cobbold sons **had a great penchant for this sport, and though quite a lad, would venture upon the most hardy enterprises with the weather-beaten sailors, who had been long-accustomed to the river. He was a good shot and would bring home many a duck and mallard as fruits of his own excursions.**

It was about four o'clock, one winter evening when this young gentleman was seen descending the steps of the Cliff with the oars over his shoulder, and his gun in his hand.

Over two hours were to pass before his father realised he was missing. Desperately concerned, a party composed of family and employees from the brewery and household went in search of him. Two men searched the dark river by boat, leaving others to call for the boy along the bank. Though it was dark and bitterly cold and it seemed as if all hope had been abandoned, Margaret, it was, who pleaded with her employer and his clerk to keep on searching.

"Pray do not give it up yet! Let us go on farther! Do not go home yet!"

About a hundred yards onwards, under the shade of a wood, they met a man.
"Who goes there?" was the question of the anxious father.

"What's that to you?" was the rough uncourteous reply, strangely grating to the father's heart at such a moment.

In those rough sounds Margaret recognized Will Laud's voice. She sprang forward, exclaiming to the no small astonishment of her master, "Oh, William! Mr. Cobbold has lost his son. Do lend a hand to find him."

"My son went down the river in a boat some three or four hours since and I fear he is lost," said Mr. Cobbold.

Will Laud had seen no boat on the river and had abandoned his own farther upstream as the 'floats of ice' had made it too dangerous to continue. At that very moment, two of the brewery men found the boy's boat abandoned. It was caught in branches, well away from the shore. There was no sign of young Master William. All they could do was continue with their search. Then, just as all were losing heart…

"What is that dark spot yonder, by the edge of the water?" said Margaret as she stooped down to let her eye glance along the dark line of the mud.

"It is only one of the buoys," said the father, "such as they moor boats to in the reach."

"There is no buoy in that part of the river," said Will. "Margaret sees something, and so do I now. I don't know what it is, but I soon will though."

And with that, he waded into the freezing ooze of the river edge, where, sure enough, he made his way to what was the stiff body of the youth they had been in search of.

Laud lost no time in hoisting the poor boy on his back and, tying his stiff hands around his own neck with his handkerchief, he crept upon the mud again toward that shore where stood those anxious friends awaiting his approach.

NARROW ESCAPE OF MASTER WILLIAM - Of all the sons of the first John Cobbold of the Cliff, Ipswich, none were so fond of the water as Master William. He was in every way cut out for a Sailor. He had a great deal of talent about him and his boat upon the Orwell was almost as well known as that of Robinson Crusoe's or Old Colson's. Many were his escapes; but this was the narrowest of them all - His father at the time had a very good offer of a Brewery at Epsom and took upon himself the responsibility of hiring William as a brewer at Epsom for which he was very unfit - and failed.

Having got into difficulties with the boat, the boy had desperately tried to make for shore and been trapped in the ooze. By the time he was carried ashore, he seemed in a desperate way, unconscious and deathly cold.

The only plan now was how to get him home as soon as they could. Laud soon constructed a carriage for him, of a hurdle, upon which he laid his own jacket, the father's greatcoat, and over him he threw Margaret's cloak. Each of the four persons taking a corner of the hurdle upon their shoulders, they made their way as fast as possible, along the shore.

CARRYING MASTER WILLIAM HOME - The incidents of this preface are so well known in the family, that they need nothing of remark - more than the wonderful nature of a poor kind-hearted boy like the Author who treasured up in his memory all that fell from the lips of his Father or Mother concerning all family events: And if a man be inscribed as a scribe to bring forth out of his treasure house things new and old and the same be instructed into the kingdom of Heaven he is no bad householder. In such spirit of love are many things collected said and done by many a good old Author. Hurrah!

Once back at the house, the boy was wrapped in warm blankets and the doctor sent for. Very gradually, life came back to the pallid cheeks of the child. In spite of his ordeal, he seemed to be well on the way to recovery.

For once in his life, Will Laud found himself the object of gratitude rather than disdain. Even so, he felt uncomfortable in such grand surroundings, looking every part the weather-beaten sailor, right down to his long man-of-war pigtail.

If the Cobbolds were anxious about having a notorious smuggler in their kitchen, they were relieved to hear that at that time, Will Laud was in the British Navy. **Such was the want of British seamen just at this period of the breaking-out of the long war, that many smugglers received not only their pardon, but good pay for joining the navy.**

Will Laud's captain had given him permission to come up to Ipswich and he had rowed as far as Nacton before abandoning his boat and coming the rest of the way on foot. He could not stay long. **He was gone before the Cliff party assembled at the breakfast table, but he took with him the best prayers of all, and most especially those of the girl of his heart, for his future safety and prosperity.**

It was not long after these occurrences that Mr. Cobbold and his family removed from the Cliff to a house in the town, a large family mansion on St. Margaret's Green.*

The adjoining park was a beautiful place. Twice a week, its gates were thrown open by the proprietor of the domain to the inhabitants of the town. During the winter, skaters would come to the round pond and mothers would bring their children, all wrapped up in coats and mufflers to watch.

One such winter's day, Mr. & Mrs. Leader came with their children to Ipswich from Brandeston. By chance, Margaret met them, to discover how much their lives had changed. They had fallen on hard times and much regretted Margaret's departure and the harsh words that had been said. Should she ever wish to return, she was told, she would be most welcome.

*The house Cobbold refers to was known as the Manor House, not to be confused with Christchurch Mansion which stands beside the park he mentions here. The round pond is still clearly identifiable in Christchurch Park today.

Margaret had ever been a prudent and careful housekeeper and those talents were to be recognised at St. Margaret's Green. A servant was soon found for the nursery, who supplied her place, and she became the active cook of the family. She had now become the head of all the domestics, from having been the servant of all. This was a true recognition of her talent and desire to be of satisfaction to her mistress.

The Manor House on St. Margaret's Green

In the garden belonging to the mansion, was a very deep pond, with turfed sides, which were sloping and steep, so that the gardener had to descend to the water by a flight of six steps.*

On the 1st June 1794, Margaret had entered the garden to gather some herbs, and had scarcely closed the gate before she heard a sudden shriek of distress. She ran down the path and there she saw the whole group standing and screaming at the edge of the pond and the nursemaid completely at her wits' end with fright. Master Henry had been running away from his sisters, his foot had caught the edge of the grass border and he had plunged into the deepest part of the pond.

Margaret showed immense presence of mind. Sending a servant for a ladder and rope, holding onto the branch of a weeping willow, she eased herself towards the centre of the pond and seized the child by the collar of his little jacket, and held him above the water until the assistance she had sent for arrived.

*This pond seems to have been within the gardens of the Cobbold Mansion, though by family tradition, the rescue was believed to have been from one of the ponds in Christchurch Park.

MARGARET SAVING THE LIFE OF MASTER HENRY - Of course I was dependent upon traditionary records of this instance of Margaret's Courage, though I believe some notice was taken of it by the public press. Master Henry was the youngest son but one of the first family. He died of decline young in life as did Rowland in the second family. Well however do I remember the weeping Willows around which I have played not only when I was a boy myself, but I have warned my own dear children of the danger as I knew the water to be deep under the willow trees - I do not know if the Old trees are still standing; But this is a faithful record of their appearance in my day.

Thus was Margaret again **the providential instrument in preserving the life of a member of Mr. Cobbold's family.**

A few days later, news came of a celebrated victory over the French. A number of Ipswich men fought in that battle. **One was poor old Jack, whose friends kept the Salutation public house in Carr Street, who always went by the name of 'What Cheer?' When he first returned home, he had his senses perfect and could speak of the engagement with clearness and precision. He was on board the same ship as William Laud and they had fought side by side. Margaret heard of this and used to go down to the public house in question to hear from Jack all she could of one who was as dear to her as her own life.**

WHAT CHEER - Here is the representation of a poor Old Man of War's Man well known in the Town and neighbourhood of Ipswich some sixty years ago. This is a faithful representation of the Old man as he stood on the Hill above the Mansion at St. Margaret's Green and the fish ponds. I believe there is a street now called Cobbold Street somewhere near this very spot - Jack Whatcheer he was called.

Margaret grew impatient awaiting Will's return. According to reports, he was at Portsmouth waiting for his prize-money and his discharge.

Some more disreputable sailors took advantage of Margaret's eagerness to hear any news of her lover and **would fabricate tales on purpose in order to get an introduction into the kitchen at St. Margaret's Green where they were sure to be welcomed and well treated by Margaret.**

Rumours spread throughout the house and, worse still, things went missing. Margaret's mistress had had enough.

"I cannot," she added, **"permit sailors of every kind to be incessantly coming to the house at all hours with pretended news of Laud."**

Margaret listened in silence and went back to her work. Then, one evening, a knock was heard at the back-kitchen door. The girl who opened it called, **"Another sailor to see you, Margaret."**

Without rising from her seat, she called, **"Tell the fellow to go about his business. I have nothing to do or say to sailors. Tell him to be off."**

The sailor pitched a canvas bag in the open doorway and left. It had a label attached addressed to her. Suddenly realising this must have been Will Laud, Margaret ran outside to where a sailor seemed to be hiding in the shadows. At first, she thought it was Will, but something wasn't right...

All too soon she realised, it had been her lover she had turned away, but another man had been following him - none other than the hated John Luff.

Luff had been waiting for Laud's return and had been watching the house where Margaret worked

The garden at the rear
of the mansion today

"Tell me where he is and I shall let you go," he warned, "but if you tell me not, down you shall go headlong into the well at the bottom of this yard."

"I do not know where Laud is. I wish I did; and I would let him know that such a villain as you are ought to be hanged."

The monster seized her, gagged her mouth with a tow-knot and heaved her into the well as he made his escape. Other servants from the house, hearing the scuffle were aware of **the bucket of the well descending with rapidity, and then a sudden splash as if a heavy body had reached the bottom of it.**

If her colleagues had not been so quick, Margaret must have drowned. As it was, she suffered a number of injuries. She was lifted from the well and put to bed. Meanwhile, the bag left by Laud was examined. It contained one hundred and thirty guineas.

It was several days before Margaret had fully recovered. It was clear she could not remain at the mansion. Leaving Will laud's money in the care of Mr. Cobbold, and with a good deal of sadness, **she took leave of as good a mistress as a servant ever had and journeyed home to join her father and brother at Nacton.**

Her father soon perceived that disappointment was gnawing at Margaret's heart. She desperately wanted to hear news of her lover's return. Jonathan Catchpole had no encouragement for his daughter.

"I much fear," said the old man, "that he has returned to the coast again and perhaps to his former vicious companions." The real problem was that no-one actually knew. Some rumours even suggested William Laud was dead.

Margaret's brother Edward was determined to help set her mind at rest and find out the truth if he could. He set off to **visit all the different places along the coast from Felixstowe to Aldeburgh.**

It did not go without notice that a young man was asking questions in the public houses best known as smugglers' haunts. Eventually, he found himself on the place known as North Vere, where he encountered the coastguardman Edward Barry. Barry did not recognise the young man but when he presented himself as Margaret's brother, was glad to meet him again.

> THE NORTH VERE* - *Some may say There never was such a place. Nor any smuggling going on as here described. All I can say, this is a fac simile of the place and scene. I have often been on the spot - but of course can never expect to be there again Nor do I desire it. But whatever improvements may take place either on the North Vere or the records of smuggling they are too well known even to many now alive to be doubted.*

In his eagerness to find the smugglers, young Edward Catchpole found himself involved in the ambush of a smuggler gang. The coastguard had spotted that a local shepherd, living on Havergate Island would raise a white flag on the shingle to indicate when the coast was clear. With no fewer than fourteen armed men hidden along the ridge, it was agreed that Edward Catchpole would raise the flag and then make sure that the shepherd should not be able to lower it again.

Now a deputy of the coastguard, he was privy to their secrets. Passing among them, using their password, 'King George for ever!' he unfurled the flag. **It was not long before a sail, which had been seen in the distance, now kept standing off and on in the offing.**

* The North Vere appears on modern maps as North Weir at the southern end of Orford Ness, opposite Shingle Street.

Margaret's brother saw the shepherd driving a score of sheep leisurely towards the flag. Though the coastguards had given him a whistle to call for help should he need it, he was able to overpower the man and force him, firmly bound, back to his cottage.

The shepherd told him he believed Will Laud was dead - he had died at the hands of John Luff. If that was so, Luff was reaping his reward at that very moment. The coastguard waited until the smugglers had all their loot ashore before launching an attack. **The firing, as they approached each other was dreadful. At last, there was one sudden tremendous yell from the boat's crew. The shout announces the leader of the smugglers to be shot and two more were lying by his side, and two surrendered, and were disarmed and guarded, whilst but one of the coastguard had fallen.**

The captain, as the reader may suppose, proved to be no other than the hated John Luff, his arm nearly cut in two, shot in the side and severely wounded on the head. He was a dying man. At last, with one wild scream, his spirit, like an affrighted bird, flew away.

Young Edward Catchpole returned to his father's home at Nacton. He carried with him the reports of Will Laud's death, but there was no firm evidence and Margaret still kept the belief that he was alive.

All this time, Margaret had been very remiss in not keeping in contact with her former employer. Mrs. Cobbold discovered she had not, as formerly intended, returned to her uncle and aunt in Brandeston. When she tried to send word to Nacton, it was on a day when Margaret and her father had visited Priory Farm and the messenger found the Catchpoles' house locked and empty.

As a result, when Margaret returned to St. Margaret's Green, she found her place filled up and her mistress reproached her for her neglect in not having had some communication with her.

Margaret moved from one position to another, briefly returning to the Cobbolds some months later. **But she was not happy. Her temper had been soured by disappointment and her spirit made restless by rumours of Laud being alive. She became impatient towards her fellow-servants, careless in her dress and manner and negligent in her work** - quite unlike the Margaret of old.

It was heartbreaking for Elizabeth Cobbold, who had so much to thank Margaret for, but the girl was much changed, and it was with great regret, she felt forced to dismiss her.

So, what had happened to Will laud in all this time? He had indeed met up with John Luff, who had offered the false hand of friendship. Believing Margaret wanted nothing to do with him, he saw himself taking up with the smugglers again. But Luff had treachery in mind and, luring Laud to a deserted spot, **attacked him, sword in hand.**

Laud defended himself with great dexterity until his sword was broken, and he himself disarmed. He fled towards the marshes, but was overtaken, cut down and cast for dead into one of those deep marsh ditches which abound in the neighbourhood of Orford.

He was fortunate to be found and carried to his uncle's house at Aldeburgh, where under the attention of the surgeon, Mr. Nursey, he made a slow but full recovery.

Here then was an opportunity - a golden opportunity for reformation. Laud's former character had been cancelled by his service in the British navy; and his gallant conduct had obtained for him a free discharge, with prize-money and a certificate of character in the service.

For two years, Will laud served as an honest seaman working for his uncle transporting timber, but following Luff's death, many were the invitations to take up again his past illicit trade. Gradually he began to run smuggling operations on that part of the coast, **though he would not head them himself.**

Margaret, this time, returned to Brandeston to help her Uncle & Aunt Leader. **She undertook once more the management of the children and was instrumental in restoring order and decency in the house. Will Laud's money was placed into the hands of the much-respected shopkeeper of the parish who placed it in the bank and became a trustee for her. Still she resolved not to touch it but to keep it, as the property of Laud, until she should be sure of his death. She had great hopes that she should one day see him again.**

Then out of the blue, a letter arrived. It was May 1797. A former fellow-servant, a coachman by the name of George Teager, claimed to have met William Laud in a public house at Ipswich.

Imagine poor Margaret's anxiety. She determined to go to Ipswich to see if it was true. She explained to her uncle the purpose of the journey.

"I fully expect to meet Laud at Ipswich, and whatever his fortunes may be, I am determined to share them with him."

She saw the old coachman and learned from him that he had seen Laud at the Salutation in Carr Street only the day before. She did not stay to ask any more questions, but off she went towards the public house.

On her way, it was her misfortune to meet with a real vagabond by the name of John Cook. One of John Luff's former associates, he was not a man to be trusted, but Margaret was so determined to find Will Laud she lost her sense of caution.

"I am in search of Laud: have you seen or heard of him today?"

"Yes, that I have; you are in luck to meet with the only person in the world who could tell you where he is."

The Salutation in Carr Street today

Poor Margaret! If only she had been less trusting. Here was another sailor only too ready to take advantage of her desire, at any cost, to find William Laud.

According to Cook, Will Laud was on the run and had taken himself off to London. Letters were produced, supposedly from Laud to Cook, asking him to send a certain *'brown nag'* to him that he might sell it. Horse-stealing was a hanging offence and Margaret should have had nothing to do with it, but John Cook was a plausible liar and Margaret believed the only way to reach her lover was to ride immediately to London.

Her first thought was to borrow a horse from old George Teager. Convinced by Cook this had to be done in secret, the pair found even their combined efforts were not enough to catch and saddle the horse. Cook then had another suggestion.

"Not many yards off in yonder stable, there are two noble horses that are worth riding. You shall take one of them."

He meant she should steal one of Mr. Cobbold's carriage horses. Naturally, she told him she dared not do as he suggested.

"Nonsense girl! If you don't come along and just do as I bid you, hang me if I don't write to Laud, and tell him you don't care any more about him."

So, with Cook's urging, Margaret crossed the stable yard, dressed herself in the coachman's stable dress and saddled one of the horses, a fine strawberry roan with cropped ears; unfortunately a striking and easily-recognized horse.

Old George, who slept over the stable, was very deaf and heavy in his sleep. He did not hear a sound as the horse was saddled and mounted. Margaret was ready to ride to meet her lover.

"Now," Cook replied, "mind what I say: you must ride to the Bull in Aldgate, London; but if you regard your own and your lover's safety, you will sell the horse first, and then find your way to the Dog & Bone public house at Lambeth; there you will find Will Laud expecting you. Sell the horse for all you can get; say he is worth a hundred guineas and that your master, Squire John Cook sent you up to sell him."

So it was, reckless of all the dangers that might await her, Margaret rode through the night; a full seventy miles in the space of just eight hours and a half. But she was noticed along the way and the horse recognized, so soon after dawn, word had reached the Cobbolds that one of their fine carriage horses had been stolen. George Teager and Mr. Spink, the dealer who had supplied the horse, were sent in pursuit. Hand-bills were printed in time to be sent on the nine o'clock coaches to London, offering twenty guineas reward for the recovery of the horse and the conviction of the offender.

MARGARET STEALING THE HORSE - We now come to the more stirring events of Margaret's most daring exploits. We have her statement of the ride she had to undertake. The task of Horse Stealing - The Horse she rode on was old crop: When I was at Cambridge over to the Market on my old White Horse A gentleman rode up to me and apologising for the intrusion said that a wager was laid at the betting post that I was upon the horse Margaret Catchpole stole. My answer was to decide. - I simply replied The Horse Margaret Catchpole stole was a crop eared horse. It was enough.

Margaret stopped just once on her journey to London; at the Trowel & Hammer at Marks Tey, to give her gallant horse a feed of corn and a drink of water. On arriving at the Bull, Aldgate, she paid an ostler to rub the horse down, whilst enquiring where she might find a buyer.

Time passed, and after Margaret had breakfasted there were potential buyers to be found. Dressed as she was, she passed easily for a male groom sent to sell a horse for his master. Figures approaching a hundred guineas were spoken of. One dealer was particularly interested. Then, with the deal still not concluded, one of the hand-bills from Ipswich arrived in the yard of the Bull, and the constables alerted.

MARGARET APPROACHING LONDON - I have in my possession many letters from various persons who met her on the road and conversed with her concerning the horse. It was at a horse dealers yard close to the Four Swans, Bishopsgate that she was taken into custody. I have my dear mother's letter to my Father giving him an account of her interview with Margaret and her conviction to take her at the next assizes at Bury St. Edmunds. All these letters! Mr. Alshor of D____ told me he was the one who saw her on the horse... and too [?] for a young jockey riding his Masters horse to L_____.

"Did you say that horse came from Ipswich, young man?" said the dealer.

"I did," said she.

"What was your master's name?"

"Mr. John Cook," said Margaret, who began to feel a little uneasy.

"Are you sure it was not Mr. John Cobbold? Look at that hand-bill young man."

Margaret saw only her master's name, and all her fortitude forsook her; she swooned away in a moment, and would have fallen from the horse, had not the constable caught her by the jacket as she was falling; and in endeavouring to support her off the horse, the jacket flew open and to the astonishment of all around her, lo, and behold, it was a woman.

Margaret was taken into custody and immediately committed to Newgate gaol

It must have come as something of a shock to Mr. and Mrs. Cobbold to discover the name of the thief responsible for stealing their horse. They journeyed to the Police Station at Whitechapel for the magistrates' examination. Margaret was quite overcome with shame and regret. She made a full confession of her guilt, stating **she had been persuaded, even compelled to this act by a man named Cook, a sailor at Ipswich, and declared she stole the horse by his direction and threats.** She did not betray her lover's name, or mention where she believed he was hiding.

> *MARGARET TAKEN INTO CUSTODY - The description of this event as given in evidence before the Magistrate at Bow Street in Mrs Cobbolds letters is much more copious than any of the meagre accounts in the public newspapers of the day. And there of course I obtained all my information. I suppose I have at home letters from various persons concerning Margaret - One ridiculous one from a Miss close of Cheltenham calling me I know not what. I simply sent her a sermon I had just published for the Diss Provident Society. Provide things honestly in the sight of all men: It lead her to enquire - and oh such a petulant letter came in reply.*

Every effort was made to find John Cook, but he had disappeared. Margaret, meanwhile, was removed to Ipswich gaol, awaiting her trial. She wrote to Elizabeth Cobbold, pleading for forgiveness, and the good lady visited her a number of times. They were both aware of the likely result of her crime. There was a good deal of horse-stealing going on, so **scarcely a week passed without rewards being offered for the apprehension of thieves.** Judges were being urged to make an example of those who were caught.

Time flew fast and the day of her trial approached. She was to depart for Bury, where the Assizes were held, early on the morning of the 9th of August 1797.

The town was a-bustle with people, and though the purpose was serious and full of foreboding, assize week was one of entertainment and rejoicing, coloured by a great deal of pomp and ceremony.

The judges entered the town, the trumpets sounded, the bells rang, and bright ornate robes and regalia were on show.

Margaret pleaded guilty for no other reason than that she was guilty. There was no denying it. Several people spoke on her behalf - Doctor Stebbing, her Uncle Leader and others. His Lordship, the judge in his summing-up, acknowledged that Margaret was the least deserving of the sentence he was bound to pass of all those he had ever tried. But at the end of the day, there could be only one result.

"It only remains for me to fulfil my duty, by passing the sentence of the court upon you which is… that you be taken from the place where you now stand, back to the place whence you came, and there to be hanged by the neck until you are dead; and may God have mercy upon your soul."

At these last words, tears of agony overwhelmed many in the court, but Margaret herself seemed calm and resigned.

The Outer Gate of
Ipswich Gaol (inset:
the Women's Prison)

> MARGARET IN THE CONDEMNED CELL - *I heard Baron Alderson say the first time he was in a court of justice was with his father in the year 1797 when Margaret Catchpole was tried. He told me, he remembered her most appearances as then before she broke out of jail as a most extraordinary person. My Mother couldn't go to the trial because I was then expected to come into the world, which I did on 9th September 1797. So my childhood was filled with hearing every one talk of the poor condemned culprit.*

Just two days later, **a letter arrived from the Home Office in London giving full powers to the judge to exercise mercy in her case, as he might see fit.**

Mr. Cobbold was sent for, and it was explained to him that Margaret's sentence would be reduced to one of transportation to New South Wales for a period of seven years.

It was suggested that as there was great difficulty at the time in sending prisoners to the new colony, she might well spend her entire confinement in Ipswich gaol, and with good behaviour, might be released much sooner.

> THE REPRIEVE - *I am very much aware people have said How could Mr. Cobbold prosecute such a person! He had no choice or alternative in the matter. He was bound over to prosecute her. And Horse stealing was carried on at that time to such an extent that the severest penalty of the law seemed to be the only prevention of the crime. Yet such was the good character given this young woman, that before the Judge left Bury a reprieve came down for and a commutation from death to 7 years transportation was the order of the court. What curious dresses the chaplain wore on that day - After wigs cocked hats and shorts and gaiters.*

Margaret wrote to Mrs. Cobbold, believing her support had helped reduce her sentence, and thanking her for her kindness. **She became very industrious and trustworthy in the service of Mrs. Ripshaw, the governor's wife; and made herself useful in every possible way to her new mistress. In fact, she became an invaluable person in the gaol.**

She still asked after Will Laud, but nothing had been heard of him. **In the winter of 1797, Margaret lost her father,** and the following spring, her brother Edward moved away to avoid his sister's notoriety. He did not want to spend the rest of his life known as the brother of a female horse thief. A certain loneliness came over Margaret. It seemed less likely that her sentence would be shortened and her spirit grew restless and anxious.

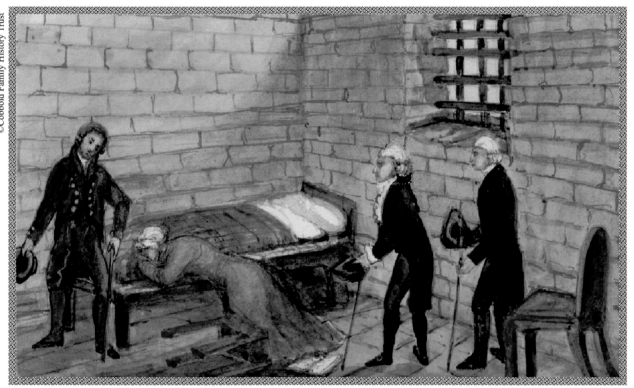

Unbeknown to Margaret, her former lover, was closer than she might have dared hope. In 1799, Will Laud was captured and held in Ipswich gaol. He was a ruined man, sentenced to pay a hundred pounds fine, yet all his possessions had been taken by the Crown. It seemed he would never be released.

Margaret had been engaged in washing for Mrs. Ripshaw. At this time, large linen-horses belonging to the gaol stood in the passage between the debtors' and the felons' yards. There it was, she saw a face she recognized. Could it be? Yes, it was. Pretending to help her with the washing, he struck up a conversation with her and learned the story that had led to her imprisonment.

There was one other matter of importance. Margaret had never touched the prize-money Laud had left with her. It would easily clear his debt and leave the two of them enough to set up home together when she was released.

She wrote to her Uncle Leader to arrange for a hundred pounds to be paid to release Will laud from his fine. But less than three years into her own sentence, it seemed her incarceration would never end.

On March 3rd 1800, a few days before her lover's release, as she hung the washing onto the huge clothes-horses, she heard a well-known voice.

"Margaret, what a capital ladder one of those horses would make, if set against the wall." She turned round and there stood Will Laud.

"Ah, William! I understand you. I wish I could make my escape with you, and I would; but I fear the thing is too difficult."

"You might manage it, Margaret, when the governor goes to Bury with the prisoners."

So an idea of escape was born. The plan was that Margaret should choose a day when the clothes racks and linen lines would be available to aid her. She would aim, after making her escape, to meet up with Will Laud, in the hope that together they could reach the house of his sister at Sudbourne. Then, it was agreed, they would take a boat to Holland together.

On the 6th March 1800, his debts paid, Will Laud was released. Margaret felt immense happiness knowing **she had been instrumental in procuring the release of her lover.**

For the next two weeks, she worked in preparation for her escape. She made clothes that would disguise her. From her sheets, she made a smock-frock such as shepherds wear and a pair of sailor's trousers.

Towards the end of March, Mr. Ripshaw departed with the prisoners for trial at Bury. He would be gone at least a week.

Tuesday 25th March was washing day. At the time for locking in, Margaret carried her disguise in a bundle into an empty adjoining cell. When the turnkey came to lock her in, she heard him call, **"Margaret , are you there?"**

She put her lips to the wall of the cell where she was, and answered, "Yes." It sounded exactly as if she was in bed in her own cell. In the darkness, it was impossible for the man to know she was calling her reply from the cell next door. As the place she was hiding was supposed to be empty, he saw no need to lock that cell.

She waited, hearing the clock strike **the hours of nine, ten, and eleven. She now rose, took her shoes in her hand and her bundle under her arm and descended the front of steps that led to the Felons' yard.**

The gaol wall was twenty-two feet high with metal spikes atop. Some time before, Margaret had spotted a gap where one of the spikes was broken off. If she was to find freedom, that was the way.

> *METHOD OF ESCAPE - It was a wonderful infatuation that possessed this poor creature. No romance could equal it. The narrative. She herself did not need to escape, nearly she had completed the term of her transportation such was her good conduct and high report of her servitude that an additional revision of the term of her imprisonment had already been intimated by the Magistrates to Ripshaw, the Jailer - But this was not to be communicated until an order in Council was made out - This may in some measure account for the unfortunate timing of her escape. Her good conduct and also the reliance placed upon her added to the facility of her escape.*

Clothes-horses had not been left out, so taking a plant-stand from the governor's garden, she placed it against the wall. It only reached halfway up, but using clothes-line and a linen-prop, she was able to put a tight noose over one of the spikes on the wall. This left her an intrepid climb, but it was just possible.

She drew herself up by the line to the top of the wall, and there she laid awhile by the part where the spike was broken.

Holding onto the rope and plunging headfirst through the gap in the spikes, she found she was then able to let herself down in perfect safety on the other side. **Was there ever such a desperate act performed by any woman before? It seems incredible, but Margaret Catchpole did exactly as here described.**

DESCENDING THE WALL - Her own account of her escape given to my mother and the evidence given in a court of Justice when she was tried for breaking out of prison, both agree; and in fact Ripshaw's evidence of what he found to be the fact all speak of her wonderful courage. The same courage afterwards displayed in the great flood in saving the life of the Leslies* - which she mentioned in one of her letters to my mother - gained for her freedom; So she became a real true free inhabitant of Australia but this is too well authenticated a fact of her escape from the Ipswich Gaol to be denied.

---

*In the book by Richard Cobbold, the family are called the Laceys

Just as she alighted on the earth, St. Clement's chimes played for twelve o'clock. She climbed over the low wooden palings against the road and made her way for the lane against St. Helen's church. There she found Will Laud in **readiness to receive her,** as they had planned.

GETTING OVER THE OUTER PALING - Here she laments a sad rent, which occasioned her some trouble. We are dependent upon her own account of what happened entirely to herself for though all external evidence corroborated her account yet so well had she managed that had not old Colson's recognition at the Woodbridge Ferry and the Ferryman's account agreed, Ripshaw, who was under a severe penalty for letting her escape, would never have caught her - As it was a sad narrative that he had to give of the eventual pursuit - But the last paling is her own account.

Margaret put on her sailor's clothes and from there the two started off for Woodbridge and the ferry that would carry them across the River Deben.

> *ON THEIR WAY TO WOODBRIDGE - We are of course dependent upon her own account of herself in this dress, and her journey to Woodbridge canfirmed as it is by Ripshaw's evidence in pursuit of his prisoner. Certain it is that he got on the right path at the Ferry early in the morning. It is certain also, that when she was taken, she was in a sailor's dress as it was. He very nearly lost all pursuit, had it not been for poor old half crazy Robinson Crusoe - alias Thomas Colson, who knew Will Laud well - and guessed who the other unsailor like person was.*

They made Woodbridge by the first light of day. **Their intention was to cross the Sutton Walks and Hollesley Heath to Sudbourne. Unluckily for them however, who should they meet at the ferry but old Robinson Crusoe, the fisherman who was compelled to come up the Deben to Woodbridge for the sale of his fish. The old man gave them no sign of recognition, but he knew them both, and with a tact that few possessed, saw how the wind blew. But without speaking to either of them, he proceeded with his basket to the town.**

The morning after Margaret's escape, the turnkey was alarmed by the call of the gardener, who came early to the prison to prune trees in the governor's garden. He told the turnkey there was a rope hanging down the wall, as if someone had escaped during the night.

All the cell doors were checked, and found to be still locked. Only when Margaret was discovered missing did Mrs. Ripshaw begin to work out what had happened. Her husband's absence made the circumstance the more distressing.

A search began. All Margaret's known haunts were tried - Brandeston, Nacton, even the places she was known to have worked. Hand-bills were printed, offering fifty pounds reward for information leading to her capture. This notice was circulated far and near and was the main topic of conversation in most places.

It so happened that some of the servants of Mrs Cobbold mentioned the subject of the reward to the old fisherman Robinson Crusoe, as he stood at the back door with his basket of fish.

"I think I may have seen her, or the foul fiend has played me one of his shabby tricks. I saw that fellow Laud and someone very like her go across the Sutton Ferry together. She might deceive anyone else, but the foul fiend showed her to me, though she was in a sailor's dress. I told your mistress that no good would come of Margaret Catchpole."

RECOGNIZED BY OLD ROBIN IN THE MORNING - *Here again we are dependent upon her own statement of the case corroborated as it was by 'Old Rips' as Ripshaw was called accounts of the pursuit: It was an untoward event. She seeing the same Old Fisherman who*

once saved her or helped save her at The Priory Farm shore at D o w n h a m Reach - The Suffolk Heroine for such she was, was saved to do some good in her generation after all this.

That was enough to set Ripshaw and a constable on their trail: a trail that led them through Eyke to where Laud's brother-in-law, Keeley, kept a flock of sheep on the marsh saltings at Sudbourne.

Keeley was a shrewd and surly fellow, deliberately evasive of their questions. Ripshaw believed Margaret and Laud were nearby but if he was to recapture Margaret Catchpole, he needed help. Fortunately, a revenue cutter, captained by Edward Barry was crossing the River Alde at that very moment. On hearing of their mission, **Barry's sense of duty compelled him to render the assistance required.**

Accordingly, they were soon seated in the stern of the boat and were being rowed towards the spot where, on the main shore, Laud and Margaret stood anxiously watching the approach of a boat from a vessel on the sea.

THE GAOLER AND PREVENTIVE SERVICEMEN - Ripshaw and the Preventive going to take Margaret off the North Vere. The public records of the County at that period before the employment of Stenographic Reporters were very meagre and the evidence given in a court of Justice, but very scant. We are therefore dependent upon Mrs. Cobbold's letters for the facts of how Margaret was taken. As may be supposed my dear Mother was much afflicted at her conduct.

No sooner had they alighted from the revenue men's boat than Ripshaw and the others spotted their quarry on the other side of the shingle. When, at the last minute, Margaret caught sight of the gaoler, with a wild shriek, she rushed into the sea, which caught her on a wave and cast her back, breathless upon the beach.

Orford Ness, from the air

MARGARET RUSHING INTO THE SEA - All this was corroborated by Ripshaw's account to the Magistrates of the recapture of Margaret. It was with great difficulty that Mrs. Cobbold obtained an interview with Margaret previous to her second trial. She was not allowed any communication with any one previous to her second trial.

Laud stood across the seemingly lifeless body of that devoted girl, and with a pistol in each hand, dared the revenue men to make prisoners of them. Seeing there was no hope of their surrender and aware of the guns pointed at them, Edward Barry issued one final warning.

The next instant, two pistols flashed and Laud lay stretched upon the sand. He had first fired at Barry and missed, and the next moment in self-defence, Barry was compelled to fire in return. The ball passed through his heart and killed him on the spot.

So ended the career of a man who, only in the few latter days of his life, seemed steadily resolved to act fairly by the woman who had devoted her life to him. Poor Susan's words at last proved true: "Margaret, you will never marry William Laud."

WILL LAUD DEFENDING THE BODY OF MARGARET - Will Laud's death. Concerning this attack, we could only go upon her own account of it, and Ripshaw's evidence. The death of many smugglers and lawless men was little thought of in that day when all Europe was in flames at the French Revolution and the dreadful doings of the Inquisition - Margaret had very little pity except from her mistress.

Margaret and her dead lover were conveyed to the Ship Inn at Orford*. Within a short space of time, she found herself back under lock and key in Ipswich gaol.   She was desolate. As she said, **"Laud is dead, my father is dead, my brother is at a distance and will probably be so ashamed of me that he will never come to see me again."**

Fortunately for Margaret, she did receive support from one person. Elizabeth Cobbold did not abandon her, and in the months leading up to her second trial, **became a frequent visitor to the gaol.**

Many crimes at that time carried the death penalty. Margaret knew only too well that escaping from a sentence of transportation was one such crime. In pleading guilty, she found His Lordship, the Judge less supportive than he had been before. In his eyes, she had already been given a chance and rejected it. Though she spoke well in her defence, for the second time in her short life, she would hear those same dreadful words condemning her to death.

*There never was a pub at Orford named 'The Ship'. Amongst assorted pub names from the past, I encountered one named 'The Lifeboat.' which ceased to trade in 1815. Possibly this was what Richard Cobbold meant.

Whether it be influence that was exercised on behalf of the prisoner, or perhaps the judge felt her life should be spared, **before he left Bury, her sentence was once more changed from death to transportation. But this time it was for life. When told of it as an act of mercy, Margaret replied that it was no mercy to her.**

A number of visitors came to see her in those last months she spent in England: Elizabeth Cobbold continued to be a great support. Her Uncle & Aunt Leader; even the Lord Chief Baron who had condemned and reprieved her twice came to the gaol, though she did not recognize him without his wigs and robes. Her brother Charles arrived from India a day too late. She had already been taken with two other female prisoners from Ipswich to Portsmouth to board the convict ship, Nile, bound for Botany Bay.

> *THE CONVICT SHIP - At last the dreaded time did arrive. The identical letter which Margaret wrote the very evening before she left the Ipswich Gaol is lodged at the public Museum in the Town of Ipswich; and I maintain that considering the materials she had and the limited education of the period it is both better written than even in these days of popular education Many a servant girl can write - It was my province to see and notice with deep feeling my fond and enlightened Mother's grief for her poor servant and to hear all the kind expressing of her pure spirit.*

Thus ended the career of Margaret Catchpole in England, where her virtues will long be remembered, together with her crimes. What remains of her history will serve to show what fruits may be gathered from a faithful spirit, a high courage and a good heart.

The years following Margaret's transportation are related by way of a series of letters that she sent to those in England still keen to keep in touch with her. Consistently among these was Elizabeth Cobbold, to whom Margaret usually referred as 'honoured Madam.'

Though she had been most melancholy about her banishment, it was a more cheerful and excited Margaret who wrote back to England, most taken with the country and her new way of life.

Initially, she worked in an orphanage in Sydney, but her talent and industry were soon recognized and she was offered the chance to care for a family of children in an area known as Richmond Hill.

MARGARET'S COTTAGE - It is astonishing with what avidity I used to hear my Mother read all Margaret's communications from Botany Bay. Her first landing, and it putting her in mind of the dear Cliff - and her only sorrow that she could not see her dear Mistress there. - It appears that she was located as the custom was to a very good place - I have all her letters labelled and dated by my dear Father who took great interest in all that concerned the poor woman. As to me I remembered things with a gusto!

From time to time, Margaret would parcel up all manner of treasures to send home to her dearest friends, especially the Cobbold family. They, by way of thanks would send her things they thought she might need in return. Months would pass between mail posted and received, and often items would be lost, but one notable case did arrive in England that contained a magnificent pair of lyre-birds, later to be presented to Ipswich Museum.

> *MANURA SUPERBA - How well do I remember the arrival of the different chests containing the different things this poor girl sent with a heart of gratitude to her mistress. I think she sent the very first skins of the Lyra Pheasant to England. The Card opposite will show the restoration of the very birds, All I can hope is that they are taken care of - To me they can be of very little interest now: but as affording the most complete evidence of the pure feeling of love that then existed.*

MANURA SUPERBA.

Lyra, or Botany Bay Pheasant.

THESE beautiful Birds were sent to the late Mrs. Cobbold of the Cliff, by Margaret Catchpole, a female servant who stole a Coach Horse from the late J. Cobbold, Esq., and rode it up to London in one night. She was in the act of selling the Horse in Town, when she was taken. She was in man's apparel. She was tried at Bury in 1797, and received sentence of death, which sentence, owing to the entreaties of the prosecutor, was changed to seven years transportation, but breaking out of goal, she was afterwards transported for life.

Presented to this Museum by R. K. Cobbold, Esq.

Margaret's adventures did not end with her banishment. Her landlady, Mrs. Palmer, was a true friend and helped her to set up her own shop and smallholding, enabling her to become truly independent.

From time to time, the calm and beauty of the countryside would be shattered by high winds and storms. A near-neighbour, Thomas Lacey and his family were, on one occasion trapped on the roof of their barn as water torrented past and threatened to wash them away. Nobody seemed prepared to help. Only at Margaret's fiercest insistence would others join her in borrowing a boat, and risk their own lives, as she was prepared to, rescuing the trapped family from the thatch and carrying them to Margaret's house which stood on higher ground, safe from the flood.

> *MARGARET'S COURAGE IN THE GREAT FLOOD - The description of this flood and its terrors, and the saving of Mr. Leslie's* family - her shaming the men into exertion on behalf of the sufferers, is most graphically described. This is in one of her best letters. - It was the cause of her being made a free woman and of the Governor's report to the home Government of what he had done. - All which was sanctioned by the Government and approved. It was not long after this that she married.*

*In the original story, the family name is Lacey

Unbeknown to Margaret, John Barry, who had all those years ago declared his undying love for her, was living nearby, and had risen to some eminence. It was ten years into her sentence before he realised she was so close. Hearing tales of her courage and the renown in which she was held; especially rescuing the Laceys from the flood; he sought a full pardon for her.

The day he presented himself to her, he reminded her of the promise he had made all those years before. He had never married, and still loved her.

It is needless, perhaps to add that Margaret Catchpole changed her name, and became the much respected and beloved wife of John Barry Esq. Of Windsor by the Green Hills of Hawkesbury.

WINDSOR LODGE ON THE HAWKESBURY - There is evidently now a difference in tone though not of affection towards her dear Mistress at the Cliff - in all her correspondence. For the first time she begins to see the joy of a really settled character - and for the sake of her most excellent husband and children to have her real name concealed. That she was a true Christian penitent I have no doubt - She was both before and after her husband's death greatly respected.

Though she had the free pardon and the right to return to England, Margaret never did. She lived out her days in comfort in her adopted country, where she became as well-known and loved as in her native Suffolk.

MARGARET AS LAST SEEN AT SYDNEY - In her last letter to her mistress she gives a description of her fortune and her affectionate children; and also a declaration of the joy it would give her to see any of her dear Mistress's Family at Sydney - Margaret herself outlived her husband a few years, and died in the same year that her dear Mistress did.

MARGARET'S FUNERAL AT SYDNEY - All things must come to an end and happiest they who live the most quiet and peaceable life in the bosom of their own families in their Christian Land - "By this," says our Saviour, "shall all men know that ye are my disciples if ye have love one to another." And without this love and Charity what is the Christian benefited - What work can he do?

This portrait of Margaret, painted by Rev. Richard Cobbold can be seen at Christchurch Mansion, Ipswich and is reproduced by kind permission of Colchester & Ipswich Museum service

A final word from the editor of this edition of Margaret Catchpole, and from the author

The story of Margaret Catchpole is full of historical inaccuracies. Richard Cobbold makes his heroine younger, prettier and more literate than she really was. He suggests, wrongly, she married the man he calls John Barry, and even had children. Working with very little evidence of her later life (her last letter was dated 1812), he gives his audience the ending they would most have wanted. He appears to have made a genuine error in confusing Margaret with another convict-made-good. For all that, the real Margaret Catchpole was a remarkable person. Her story had captivated the people of Suffolk long before Richard Cobbold committed it to a novel. Though he was too young ever to have known her, so many of the people he grew up with would have helped build this story in his mind, until he was ready to tell it, embracing the romantic tradition that characterised Victorian literature.

Two hundred years have elapsed since Margaret's crimes; one hundred and fifty since the story became a best-seller. It continues to be Richard Cobbold's most lasting memorial. Now, after all this time, the primitive charm of his water-colours helps the reader to imagine Suffolk at the time of Nelson and Constable and Margaret Catchpole.

Pip Wright

REMARKS BY THE AUTHOR - I cannot conclude this book without an observation or two worthy of remark. I have two letters from the Misses Hopes of Glasgow Merchants; in the first of which they tell me, they almost wished that their relative had been Margaret Catchpole but that she certainly was not because her maiden name was Mary Haydock. She was transported from Bury in Lancashire and hence the confusion of the persons. But now by way of something of less consequence - My brother Charles saw this lady on board a Leith Packet and spoke to her as if she had been the identical Margaret Catchpole - When she found herself mistaken for Margaret she emphatically insisted Mr. Hope threaten me with action for libel but I got out of the scrape more easily than she got into it. - The Bishop of Sydney also wrote to me upon the subject but I had no difficulty in explaining the Truth as it really was! - and so Farewell.

RC

Some of Richard Cobbold's misconceptions regarding Margaret's later life arose from the fact he confused her with a girl from Bury in Lancashire called Mary Haydock. Margaret had been tried and sentenced in Bury in Suffolk and it is easy to see how such a mistake could be made. Mary Haydock, later known as Mary Reiby, became rich and famous in a way Margaret Catchpole never did.

Appendix - A few of the characters who appear in this book

In addition to Margaret Catchpole herself, quite a lot is known about a number of the characters in this book, who were very much real people, as she was. Newspapers of the time and other sources give us further information about these people.

Doctor Stebbing: According to ninetenth century Ipswich historian, John Glyde, one Dr. Stebbing, who lived in a house *'in front of the Catholic Church'*, was a crack-shot and greatly looked forward to the start of the shooting season on September 1st, to such an extent he was reluctant to treat patients that day. Any who did seek his attention, would get short and summary treatment. He was a man accustomed to rising early and believed others should do the same. As a result he refused to pay any tradesman who appeared with a bill after eight in the morning, saying they were lazy and needed to get up earlier if they expected to be paid by him.

Thomas Colson: At his death in 1811, a Suffolk Chronicle obituary read, *'Thursday sen'night, Thomas Colson, (more generally known by the appellation of Robinson Crusoe) a disordered man who was originally a woolcomber, for many years had followed the occupation of a fisherman on the River Orwell, was lost near Levington Creek; his little shattered bark having got upon a mud bank, was afterwards sunk by the ebbing of the tide. Having been attacked by a nervous fever about 18 years ago, his mind has been in a state of derangement ever since, nor could he be persuaded* *but that he laboured under the power of witchcraft; and to guard against its effects, he constantly wore the bones of animals and old iron sewn up and bound round him, which made his appearance very romantic.*

Notwithstanding his mind was evidently disordered, he yet retained a strong mechanical genius: he was the builder of his own craft: had also learned to weave; nay his ingenuity even extended to the construction of musical instruments, having made many violins for sale: an organ which he had brought to tolerable perfection was his last attempt in that line. Poor Robinson's boat has been raised, but his body has hitherto eluded the most vigilant search: it is supposed he was washed off the deck. This eccentric character was in his 57th year, perfectly inoffensive, and free from that sin of blasphemy to which seafaring men are too often addicted.

According to the Suffolk Garland, Colson was tall and thin with piercing eyes. His whole body, it was said, was encircled with charms, bones, stones with holes in them and spells and verses to protect him from his tormentors.

John Ripshaw: The gaoler at what was then the new gaol at Ipswich, Ripshaw was a fit, strong athletic man. Ipswich Journals of the late 18th century describe him leading intrepid chases after escaped criminals. He hunted down Lay and Hoy in 1779 and Charles Turner in 1790. In those cases, as with Margaret Catchpole, he would have stood to lose a substantial surety (Cobbold says 500 pounds) for losing a prisoner. Cobbold describes Ripshaw as a keen gardener, raising carnations, ranunculuses and polyanthuses. Following his death aged 56 in may 1801, an advert offered his collection of auriculas and carnation plants. He also grew prize-winning fruit.

Elizabeth Cobbold: She married John Cobbold after his first wife had died, leaving him with fourteen children. She too was a widow, but then this second marriage produced another seven offspring, of whom Richard Cobbold was one. She was a great champion of the arts and of her chosen charities. Her home was always alive with visitors - artists, writers and musicians. She wrote a good deal of poetry and appears in Dickens' Pickwick Papers thinly disguised as 'Mrs. Leo Hunter.' Her works were regularly published in the local press, including one poem dedicated, on his death, to Thomas Colson, 'Old Robinson Crusoe.'

> *...I may not sleep - with hellish pow'r, the wizard works in secret bow'r*
> *I saw the wretch a mass prepare of melted wax and dead men's dust;*
> *From mould'ring skulls he scraped the hair and worms from eyeless sockets thrust;*
> *Then shap'd - distinct and true; I saw my very image rise;*
> *My swelling brow, my sunken eyes, too soon to dreadful likeness grew...*

John Luff and William Laud: These two are shadowy figures about whom it has been hard to find reliable evidence. People have doubted whether they actually existed. In his first edition of the book, Cobbold, as a footnote, includes a page from the smugglers' log-book, but we have no idea from where he obtained this. Laud and Luff are familiar surnames from coastal Suffolk and without their existence, it is hard to account for much of Margaret's behaviour. Almost certainly, Margaret was not born at Nacton, as the book suggests, but at Hoo near Brandeston, the home of her Uncle Leader. This was also the home of George Cullum, organiser of much of the smuggling in Suffolk at that time. Perhaps this was the true name of the mysterious Captain Bargood whom Cobbold describes running the smugglers' operations.

THE COBBOLD FAMILY HISTORY TRUST

The COBBOLD FAMILY HISTORY TRUST has three main purposes - Firstly, to collect and preserve, safely and permanently, family memorabilia: books, pictures, photographs, papers and artefacts. It was started to accept the settlor's own collection, but has since grown by acquisition and gift. Donors have often expressed relief and satisfaction that lifelong and treasured possessions have found a safe and permanent home. The Trust is non-aggressive; it does not seek items with which the owner does not wish to part, but it actively seeks items that would otherwise be lost, destroyed or fragmented.

Secondly, the Trust wishes to grow the family tree to the point where it can be beneficially published. Thirdly, and resulting mainly from the first two objectives, the Trust provides a substantial resource for family members and family historians in this and future generations.

In this fast changing world of expendability, obsolescence and disposability the remarkable and historically important family possessions of the past will vanish unless we bring them together and make them safe now. To achieve this the Trust relies solely on donations from friends and family members.

For further information on the work of the Trust, see the website at **www.cobboldfht.com**

As building a family history is inevitably a step-by-step process, readers who feel they have a contribution to make are positively encouraged to contact the Cobbold Family History Trust at:

14, Moorfields, Moorhaven, Ivybridge, Devon PL21 0XQ, United Kingdom